BOLD GRATITUDE

THE JOURNAL DESIGNED FOR YOU & BY YOU

LAINIE ROWELL
(YOUR GRATITUDE GUIDE)

&

ALLYSON LIU
(YOUR ARTSY ADVISOR)

Bold Gratitude: The Journal Designed for You & By You
© 2023 Lainie Rowell and Allyson Liu

The advice and strategies presented in this journal may not be suitable for your specific situation, and it is recommended that you seek the advice of a medical professional if necessary. The publisher and author are not responsible for any financial loss or commercial damages, including but not limited to special, incidental, consequential, or other damages.

> This book is available at special discounts when purchased in quantity for educational purposes or for use as premiums, promotions, or fundraisers. For inquiries and details, contact the publisher at books@impressbooks.org.

Published by IMPress, a division of Dave Burgess Consulting, Inc. IMPressbooks.org
DaveBurgessConsulting.com
San Diego, CA

Paperback ISBN: 978-1-948334-66-2

Cover design by Allyson Liu Creative
Interior design by Allyson Liu Creative
Edited and produced by Reading List Editorial
ReadingListEditorial.com

THIS JOURNAL IS DESIGNED FOR & BY

_____

A Note from Your Gratitude Guide

I can guess what you might be thinking...Another gratitude journal?
I know, I know, there are already sooooooooo many gratitude journals
out there!

Here's the thing: I couldn't find one that felt like it was meant for me.

To be fair, it's pretty much impossible to make something that is a perfect
fit for everyone. That's when it hit me...I could create a journal with
choices galore and serve up a buffet of options to:

- FLOOD THE BRAIN WITH HAPPINESS CHEMICALS

- TAKE RELATIONSHIPS TO THE NEXT LEVEL

- AND MAKE THE WORLD A LEGIT BETTER PLACE!

So here's what's in store for you: you can pick and choose which pages
float your boat and also tailor things to your liking. It's like having your
own personal journal genie granting your every wish!

Xo,
LAINIE

While we're at it, let's do this thing like a boss! Here are some fun supplies you may want to bust out:

- [ ] STICKY NOTES IN DIFFERENT COLORS AND SHAPES
- [ ] COLORED PENCILS AND CRAYONS
- [ ] GEL PENS OR WATER-BASED MARKERS
  (PERMANENT MARKERS LIKE SHARPIES WILL SEEP THROUGH THE PAGES)
- [ ] SCISSORS
- [ ] TAPE (E.G., DECORATIVE WASHI TAPE IS A GOOD TIME!)
- [ ] GLUE STICKS
- [ ] NOVELTY ERASERS

Now let's get started!

ONE THING I AM GRATEFUL
FOR RIGHT NOW IS...

Ways You ~~Should~~ Could Use This Journal

Great news...There's no rulebook for using this journal! You can flip to the last page and work backward, skip around like a bunny, or go in order like a military drill sergeant.

BTW, feel free to jump out of the journal, too. Whip out your notes app, record a voice memo, take a photo/video, or grab a spare piece of paper and get ready to tape, glue, or staple your way to journaling bliss! The options are endless, and the choices are yours.

This journal has something for everyone:

- FILL IN THE BLANKS
- CREATIVE ACTIVITIES
- INSPIRING QUOTES
- PROMPTS THAT MAKE YOU GO, "HMMM..."
- REFLECTIONS AND INTENTIONS

And while it doesn't cover every gratitude practice out there, there's plenty to choose from, so have fun expressing yourself however you want.

If you find something you like, you might want to stick with it for a while. Maybe even remix it to add your own spin on it!

Like a lot of variety? Each page can be a one-and-done. Simply complete it and move on.

Find a page you can't stand? Feel free to scribble all over it and/or cut it out and throw it away. Go ahead...I promise not to look, so you won't hurt my feelings.

Permission Slips

This type of permission slip, made popular by researcher and storyteller Brené Brown, is notes you write to yourself that say, "It's okay to do this thing!" They can help you feel brave and confident about trying new things, like this epic journal you are designing!

Here are some examples:

- I GIVE MYSELF PERMISSION TO BE AS CHEESY AND CLICHÉ AS I WANT.

- I GIVE MYSELF PERMISSION TO DOODLE AND DRAW IN MY JOURNAL, EVEN IF MY ARTISTIC SKILLS ARE MORE STICK FIGURES THAN PICASSO.

- I GIVE MYSELF PERMISSION TO READ BACK THROUGH MY OLD ENTRIES, TO REMIND MYSELF OF ALL THE GOOD IN MY LIFE AND HOW FAR I'VE COME.

What do you give yourself permission to do?

Permission Slip

I, _____

(YOUR NAME)

give myself permission to _____

_____

_____

(SIGNATURE)

NOTE: This is not like a promise or a guarantee that you have to do it. It's just for writing down so you remember what you are trying to do. And if you don't do it, that's okay, too! No worries, no punishment!

5-2-5 Breathing

Let's do the 5-2-5 breathing exercise! Take a deep breath in for 5 seconds, hold it for 2, then breathe out deeply for 5 seconds. Ready? Let's go! Inhale...2...3...4...5...hold...and exhale...2...3...4...5. Great job! Let's do it again!

Here's a fun idea: Cut these little reminder cards out and stick them on your bathroom mirror, your nightstand, or anywhere you need a little nudge. Enjoy the reminder to take a break and connect with your breath!

5-2-5

5-2-5

5-2-5

5-2-5

❝ Be thankful for what you have: you'll end up having more. If you concentrate on what you don't have, you will never ever have enough. ❞

OPRAH WINFREY

Origami Corner Bookmark

SUPPLIES: A square sheet of paper. You can use any size paper, but a six-inch square works well.

INSTRUCTIONS:

1. First, lay your paper flat like a diamond, not a square. (Pattern side down if you are using paper with a design.)

2. Bring the bottom corner/point of the diamond all the way up to meet the top corner/point and make a serious crease/fold mark at the bottom. When you're done, you'll have a triangle.

3. Now, bring the bottom-right corner/point to the top corner/point and make another crease.

4. Bring the bottom-left corner/point to the top corner/point and crease. (Check it out, it looks like a diamond again!)

5. Open to get back to the triangle shape, but with important creases.

6. Bring one flap down from the top to meet the bottom. **NoTE**: Not the whole thing...just the flap that is on top; it will still look like a triangle, but you'll have one part folded over.

7. Now take the bottom right and tuck it into the piece that you just pulled down from the top. (It will fold right over with half still visible and the other half hidden inside.)

8. Then repeat with the bottom left.

9. Woo hoo! Your corner bookmark is finished. Don't you feel so accomplished?

10. If you like, you can now decorate it!

PRo TIP #1: Always make legit creases because that helps as you go.

PRo TIP #2: You can use any color or patterned paper to make your origami bookmark, and you can decorate it with stickers, markers, or other embellishments (if you like) to show the things you love and are grateful for.

PRo TIP #3: If you want to challenge yourself, find some online tutorials to make origami bookmarks in the shapes of hearts, butterflies, and more!

INTRO

(UNLESS YOU DECIDE TO SKIP IT, BUT I THINK
YOU'LL LIKE IT IF YOU GIVE IT A TRY)

Notice, Think, Feel, Do

Psychologist Andrea Hussong and her crew have identified Notice-Think-Feel-Do as the four essential components of the gratitude experience, so let's get started by picking a topic and having a go at the questions below.

Check out this example:

What do you NOTICE in your life that you can be mega grateful for?

WHOA! LOOK AT THAT! MY BFF, KENDALL, GOT ME MY FAVORITE

BEVERAGE FROM THE LOCAL CAFÉ!

THINK real hard about why the universe dropped this amazing person/place/thing in your lap.

HMMM, WHY WOULD SHE DO THAT? OH, WAIT A MINUTE! I HELPED

HER WITH THAT PROJECT LAST WEEK! THIS MIGHT BE HER WAY OF

SAYING THANK YOU!

How do you FEEL about this blessing/gift?

YAY! THAT'S SO THOUGHTFUL OF HER! I FEEL SO LOVED THAT SHE

REMEMBERED MY SPECIAL DRINK.

What can you DO to show some appreciation? Make it a party and come up with some fun ways to spread gratitude!

I GOTTA RETURN THE FAVOR! TOMORROW, I'M BRINGING KENDALL

SOME YUMMY TREATS! SHE TOTALLY DESERVES IT!

Notice, Think, Feel, Do

Here are some topics to inspire you:

Everyday Things, Family, Friends, Health, Coincidences, Nature, Experiences, Tough Times, Places, Pets, Life Lessons

What do you NOTICE in your life that you can be mega grateful for?

_____

_____

_____

THINK real hard about why the universe dropped this amazing person/ place/thing in your lap.

_____

_____

_____

How do you FEEL about this blessing/gift?

_____

_____

_____

What can you DO to show some appreciation? Go all out and come up with some fun ways to spread gratitude!

_____

_____

_____

> **"A lot of people think what they need is intensity, but what they really need is consistency."**
>
> JAMES CLEAR

Creating a Journaling Habit

Full disclosure: your first week trying something new (even something really fun like this journal) can feel like a trip on the struggle bus. So, hang in there and keep on keepin' on! You can do this! Want help?

Make a plan for using this journal—your journal—in vivid detail.

When will you do it?

_____

Could you do this first thing in the morning? Not a morning person? I feel ya! Mornings do set the tone for our entire day, but really any time of day works, including bedtime! Note: Sticking to the same time every day may work best for you.

Where will you do it?

_____

Will you use your journal inside or outside? Do you have a favorite spot? Do you need a quiet space?

How will you do it?

_____

Really visualize it and see all the details: everything from where you are sitting to the writing implement you are holding in your hand. Can you picture it in your mind like you're watching a super cool movie?

PRo TIP: Highlight your responses for a quick reminder!

Gratitude in Action

Sketch yourself practicing gratitude with ~~this~~ YOUR journal. Not feeling artsy? Consider taking a quick selfie journaling. Then print it and stick it in here!

PRO TIP: Consider cutting this page out and sticking it somewhere really visible like the first place your eyes go when you wake up or by your nightstand so you see it before bed.

Let's Do This!
(A PLEDGE TO MYSELF)

I, _____
(YOUR NAME)

promise myself that I will use my journal for at least five days in a row

starting _____
(DATE)

This is a big deal to me, and it's worth my time because

_____

_____

_____

_____

_____
(YOUR WHY)

If I do five days in a row, I will be super proud of myself and will treat

myself to _____

_____

_____

_____
(YOUR REWARD)

> **❝** The key to growth is to learn to make
> promises and to keep them. **❞**
>
> STEPHEN R. COVEY

Habit Tracker

By now, you've made a pinkie promise to yourself. You might want a visual reminder, too!

While we're at it, you are what you repeatedly do, so choose your habits wisely! Let's make them fabulous!

Use this habit tracker to help yourself build good habits and reach your goals. "Practice Gratitude" is already added for you so you can color your way to thirty-one days of more joy!

What other habits do you want to add/keep?

- **NOURISHMENT:** Chow down on a balanced diet filled with yummy fruits, veggies, whole grains, lean protein, and healthy fats.

- **WATER:** Guzzle that agua like it's going out of style! Stay hydrated, baby!

- **EXERCISE:** Move that body!

- **SLEEP:** Catch some zzz's and give your body the rest it needs to take on the day.

- **MEDITATE:** Take some time to focus and get centered. Your mind will thank you for it.

Color a square for each day you nailed it!

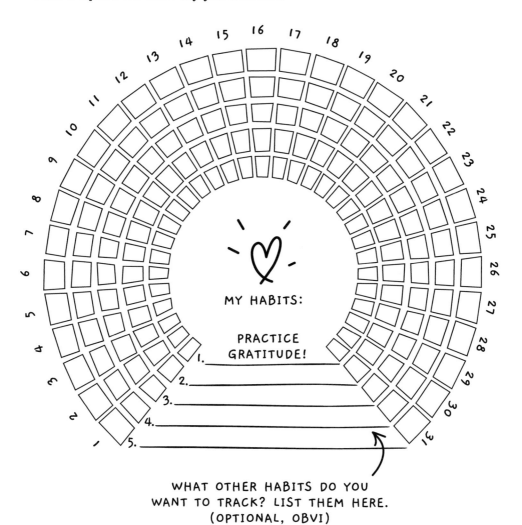

MY HABITS:

PRACTICE
GRATITUDE!

1._____
2._____
3._____
4._____
5._____

WHAT OTHER HABITS DO YOU
WANT TO TRACK? LIST THEM HERE.
(OPTIONAL, OBVI)

HAPPIER WITH GRATITUDE

Noticing the Good

(Inspired by and adapted from an activity in *The Little Book of Gratitude* by the brilliant Dr. Robert A. Emmons.)

The other day, I felt amazing when

_____

(WRITE THE PERSON'S NAME)

took the time / made the effort to

_____

(BRIEF DESCRIPTION OF WHAT THIS PERSON DID)

I know that this person could have

_____

(ANOTHER CHOICE THAT PERSON COULD HAVE MADE)

but lucky for me, this person chose to

_____

(ANOTHER BRIEF DESCRIPTION OF WHAT THIS PERSON DID)

This act

_____

(DESCRIBE HOW IT AFFECTED YOU PRACTICALLY)

and made me feel

_____

(DESCRIBE HOW IT AFFECTED YOU PERSONALLY)

Thank you

_____

(WRITE THE PERSON'S NAME AGAIN)

☐ GRATITUDE IN ACTION: Call, text, or email this person to send them your appreciation, and check the box when the mission is completed!

You can use this space to brainstorm all the people, places, and things that you notice bring you joy and make your life better.

PRO TIP: This journal is designed for you and by you, so have at it. You could list, draw, and/or use images cut out from a magazine. You can tape, glue, and/or staple to add items to this page and any other page you like. There are no rules!

> **"** Embrace your inner three-year-old! **"**
>
> NEIL PASRICHA

Small, Yet Awesome Joys

(Inspired by Neil Pasricha's blog and books)

Do you remember when you were a wee little one? Didn't everything seem magical? Let's get back to that!

To start, have you ever experienced any of these small, yet awesome joys?

- ☐ POPPING BUBBLE WRAP
- ☐ FINDING MONEY YOU FORGOT YOU HAD
- ☐ WATCHING A HILARIOUS VIDEO ON THE WEB
- ☐ WEARING BRAND-NEW SHOES
- ☐ SEEING A CUTE DOG ON THE STREET
- ☐ GETTING INTO BED WITH FRESH SHEETS THAT ARE STILL WARM FROM THE DRYER
- ☐ SPYING SOMETHING YUMMY HIDDEN IN THE BACK OF THE FRIDGE
- ☐ OPENING A TEXT NOTIFICATION TO FIND A PHOTO/MEME/GIF THAT MAKES YOU SNORT-LAUGH

Spend some time jotting down awesome little joys in your life.

If you're not sure where to start, think about coincidences, experiences, nature, learning, etc.

PRO TIP: You can keep coming back to this page until there's no trace of white left. And when that happens, you can break out the sticky notes to add even more!

Savoring Isn't Just for Food

Did you know that we can make every moment count by creating our own little savoring rituals? Yup, just focus on the details, like how things look, smell, sound, feel, or taste. Who knew that savoring the little things could be so fun and easy?

What everyday moments have you savored in the past week?

- [ ] WATCHING A BEAUTIFUL SUNSET OR SUNRISE
- [ ] LISTENING TO YOUR FAVORITE SONG OR PODCAST
- [ ] HUGGING SOMEONE YOU LOVE
- [ ] FEELING THE SOFTNESS OF A COZY BLANKET
- [ ] HAVING A GOOD LAUGH WITH FRIENDS OR FAMILY
- [ ] FEELING THE WARMTH OF THE SUN ON YOUR SKIN
- [ ] _____

When we get in the practice of savoring, we train our brains to be present and grateful.

The next few pages offer a few ideas for practicing. If you really want to. It's still totally up to you!

Joy Playlist 🎵

Jot down some song titles or favorite lyrics from the music you want to savor!

_____

_____

_____

Mindful Nature Walk

Go on a scavenger hunt for small, interesting items that you can tape, glue, and/or staple on this page. Get as abstract as you'd like!

Get Artsy Using Colors You Savor!

Stay in the lines or don't. Your call!

Yummy Grub

SAY CHEESE!

Next time you want to savor a meal, pull out your device and take a pic! After you've enjoyed it to the fullest, attach your pic here and write about it to capture all the tasty details. No devices allowed at the dinner table? No prob, just sketch the meal instead.

Create Your Own Savoring Ritual!

Spend a few moments thinking about the little things that light you up. What everyday stuff makes you feel happy and joyful?

Jot those activities down here:

_____ _____

_____ _____

_____ _____

When you're savoring, make sure to give it your full attention and ditch any distractions like your phone. (I know—Yikes!)

Trust me, you don't want to miss out on the good stuff. So, when you're in the moment, try to filter out any negative thoughts and focus on all the good things—the sights, smells, sounds, feels, and tastes.

Let's make life a little more fabulous by picking two awesome experiences to savor every day for at least two weeks. It's time to make another pinkie promise!

I promise myself that I will savor _____

and _____

for at least fourteen days in a row starting _____

_____

(SIGNATURE)

Check the days of the week to keep yourself on track.

☐ SUNDAY	☐ SUNDAY
☐ MONDAY	☐ MONDAY
☐ TUESDAY	☐ TUESDAY
☐ WEDNESDAY	☐ WEDNESDAY
☐ THURSDAY	☐ THURSDAY
☐ FRIDAY	☐ FRIDAY
☐ SATURDAY	☐ SATURDAY

Yay! You did it! Now, think about this: What positive emotions have you experienced from your savoring rituals? Capture them here:

_____   _____

_____   _____

_____   _____

It's time to give yourself some major props for being an absolute pro at savoring life. This calls for giving yourself a high five!

PRO TIP: You can always use your origami bookmark (directions in the beginning of your journal) to remind yourself to come back to this page and check the boxes!

(I learned about creating savoring rituals from the folks at PositivePsychology.com!)

Notice, Think, Feel, Do

WHAT DO YOU NOTICE IN YOUR LIFE THAT
YOU CAN BE MEGA GRATEFUL FOR?

THINK REAL HARD ABOUT WHY THE UNIVERSE DROPPED
THIS AMAZING PERSON/PLACE/THING IN YOUR LAP.

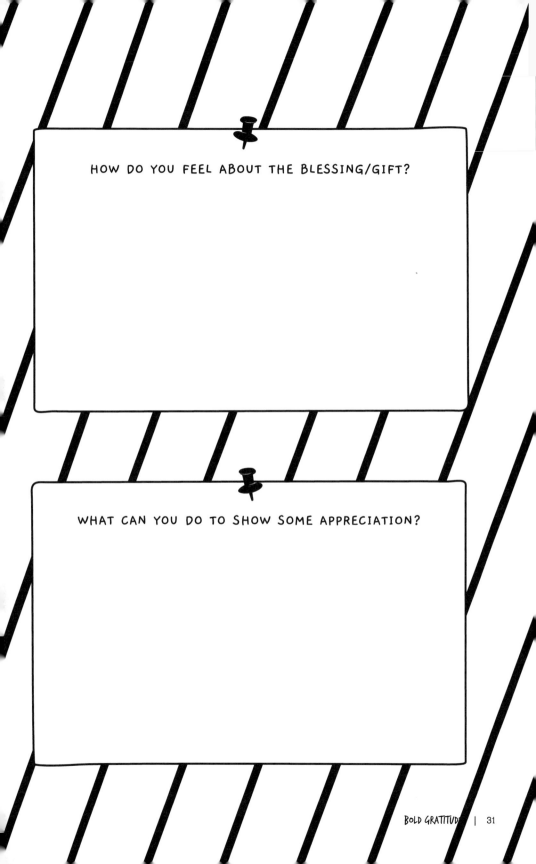

HOW DO YOU FEEL ABOUT THE BLESSING/GIFT?

WHAT CAN YOU DO TO SHOW SOME APPRECIATION?

Self-Care Challenge

Part of being grateful for ourselves is taking care of ourselves!

Which of the activities below are calling your name?

Now, figure out a way to work at least two or three of these into your week. Check the boxes when you've completed the challenge.

☐ ME TIME:
Take yourself on a solo adventure, like a hike, a museum visit, or a movie night.

☐ INDULGE:
Treat yourself to something you've been wanting for a while (a new book, a fancy beverage, etc.).

☐ LITTLE GIFTS:
Buy yourself a bouquet of flowers or a sweet treat just because.

☐ VOLUNTEER:
Volunteer for a good cause! You'll feel amazing knowing that you've made a positive impact.

☐ HUG IT OUT:
Give yourself a twenty-second hug.

☐ GET COZY:
Take a relaxing bubble bath or surround yourself with soft blankets, cozy clothes, and comfortable spaces.

☐ LOVE NOTES:
Write yourself love notes and leave them in places you will find them.

" Happiness is not what makes us grateful.
It is gratefulness that makes us happy. **"**

BROTHER DAVID STEINDL-RAST

Check It Out—I'm Living the Dream! Here's Why . . .

Use this page to capture (list, draw, etc.) all the amazing things in your life right now. Nothing is too small or too big!

You can revisit this page and add to it at will. You may even want to grab a device and take a pic of this to revisit it when you need a boost and you are away from your journal.

OMGosh, things that are out of my control and totally stressing me out right now are...

Use this page to capture (list, draw, etc.) the stress.

"Not today, Satan, not today!"

It's time to let it go! Cut this page out and destroy it! Rip it, crumple it, play trashcan basketball with it...Go wild!

Here's the deal: we're not trying to ignore the things that are bothering us. No way! What we're doing is focusing on the things that we can actually control and overcoming the negative stuff that's out of our hands.

Affirmations

Hey there, let's give ourselves some love! Self-affirmations are a great way to boost your confidence and feel good about yourself. Here are some examples:

- I AM A BOSS!
- I AM AN EXCEPTIONAL HUGGER!
- I AM CAPABLE OF ACHIEVING MY GOALS!
- I AM STRONG, INSIDE AND OUT!
- I AM PUTTING KINDNESS AND JOY OUT INTO THE WORLD!
- I AM UNIQUE AND, AS SNOOP SAYS, "THERE IS NO ONE BETTER TO BE THAN MYSELF"!
- I AM LOVED AND APPRECIATED!
- I AM A TOTAL ROCKSTAR!
- I AM WORTHY OF SUCCESS AND HAPPINESS!
- I AM DOING MY BEST, AND I'M ENOUGH!
- I AM A SUPERHERO IN DISGUISE!

Remember, you're awesome and deserving of all the good things that life has to offer. So go ahead and give yourself a little pep talk whenever you need it.

What else could you tell yourself?:

_____

_____

_____

_____

Three Things

A common gratitude practice is to list "three good things." Let's take that to the next level and make some unique "three things" lists by adding a new word in front of things.

Think about the last twenty-four hours of your life, and pick one of the "Three Things" below to fill out.
Come on back when you're ready to do another one.

THREE LOL THINGS

1. _____

2. _____

3. _____

THREE KIND THINGS

1. _____

2. _____

3. _____

THREE EPIC THINGS

1. _____

2. _____

3. _____

Want more variety? Make up your own lists! (For example, Three Unexpected Things or Three Peaceful Things.)

"Look around, look around at how lucky we are to be alive right now!"

LIN-MANUEL MIRANDA,
HAMILTON: AN AMERICAN MUSICAL

Found Poetry

Cut out letters and/or words from magazines and newspapers to create found poetry below about something you love.

> **"** Happiness can be found even in the darkest of times, if one only remembers to turn on the light. **"**
>
> ALBUS DUMBLEDORE

Meditation with a Spark

Reading with your eyes closed is not really a thing, so why not grab a voice recording app instead? You can calmly and compassionately record yourself reading this meditation, so you can listen to it when you're ready to meditate. And guess what? You can keep the recording on your device and have it ready to go whenever you need it! If you know someone with a super soothing voice, go ahead and ask them to record it for you.

~~~~~~~~~~~~~~~~~~~~~~~~~~~~~~~~~~~~~

Get in a comfy seated position, take a deep breath in through your nose, hold it for a moment, and then exhale out of your mouth with a big "Ahh."

Close your eyes and take a few deep breaths in and out. Feel your body relaxing with each exhale.

As you sit there, think of one thing you're grateful for today. It could be something small or big—anything that brings you joy. Maybe it's a sunny day, a loved one, or even just having a roof over your head.

Now, imagine that gratitude as a little spark inside of you. See that spark grow bigger and bigger with every breath you take. Feel that warmth and joy spreading throughout your body.

Take a moment to think of another thing you're grateful for, and let that spark grow even more. Keep doing this with as many things as you'd like, and watch that gratitude expand within you.

Now, let's have some fun! Imagine yourself doing a happy dance, as if you just received the best news ever. Maybe it's a little shimmy, or maybe it's a full-on dance party. Whatever it is, let loose and have some fun!

As you dance, in your mind, feel that gratitude radiating from you and spreading out into the world. Picture yourself surrounded by a bubble of love and gratitude, and know that you are attracting even more positivity into your life.

Take one more deep breath in, hold it for a moment, and then exhale with a big smile on your face. Whenever you're ready, slowly open your eyes and return to the present moment.

Take a moment to appreciate the feeling of gratitude and joy that you've cultivated through this meditation, and carry it with you as you go about your day.

~~~~~~~~~~~~~~~~~~~~~~~~~~~~~

PRO TIP: Not feeling the voiceover vibes? Let's make it easy. Visit **www.lainierowell.com/boldgratitude** for the meditation.

" Gratitude is the memory of the heart. **"**

SAINT MARY EUPHRASIA PELLETIER

A Chain of Grateful Memories

Write a memory you are grateful for on each strip and decorate them as you like. Then, cut each strip out. Next, loop one strip with your gratitude facing outward and tape it closed. Thread the next strip through the first loop and create another loop. Repeat with the rest of the strips. Voilà, you've made your gratitude paper chain.

Pick Your Prompt

When you are in the mood to free-write, pick a prompt from below and respond using the blank-ish pages that follow. You could cut the prompt out and glue or tape it on the page, giving yourself as much space as you need/want to respond. If the idea of cutting your journal stresses you out, feel free to rewrite the prompts instead.

MY LIFE IS ALREADY LEGIT AWESOME AND ONE BIG REASON IS...

OH WOW, I LOVE WHERE I LIVE BECAUSE...

I'M ACTUALLY LOWKEY PROUD OF MYSELF FOR...

3 THINGS THAT ARE LIT ABOUT BEING THE AGE I AM RIGHT NOW...

ONE THING MAKING ME GO "YASSS, LIFE!" IS...

DANG, I TOTALLY LUCKED OUT AND HIT THE JACKPOT WHEN...

SOMEONE I LOOK TO BECAUSE THEY'RE TOTALLY ROCKING THIS WHOLE "BEING HAPPY WITH WHAT YOU HAVE" THING IS...

MY BRAIN GOES "WHOA, LIFE'S RAD" WHEN I SEE, HEAR, OR FEEL...

A TIME WHEN THINGS WERE REAL BANANAS BUT I CAME OUT ON THE OTHER SIDE LIKE A BOSS WAS...

THE BOOK/SONG/MOVIE THAT I'M TOTALLY OBSESSED WITH IS...

IT'S LIKE I'VE GOT A SECRET STASH OF MAGIC DUST THAT MAKES ME SUPER SPECIAL BECAUSE I...

SOMETHING AROUND ME RIGHT NOW THAT'S MAKING ME GO, "DANG, THIS IS AMAZING!" IS...

WHEN I'M LIKE, "THAT'S IT, I'M GOOD," AND I STOP TRYING TO FIND MORE, BETTER, OR DIFFERENT STUFF, I...

PRO TIP: You can pick a new prompt each time, return to your fave(s), or both.

Reflections

Think about your last week or month.

How's it been going?

A HIGHLIGHT WAS...

A CHALLENGE WAS...

I WAS CRUSHIN' IT WHEN...

SOMETHING THAT I'VE
RECENTLY LEARNED ABOUT
MYSELF IS...

Intentions

Think about your next week or month.

What will you make happen?

SOMETHING THAT I'VE BEEN PUTTING OFF THAT I CAN DO TODAY IS...

A NEW SKILL OR HOBBY I'D LIKE TO TRY IN THE NEAR FUTURE IS...

ONE WAY I WILL APPRECIATE THE SMALL THINGS IN LIFE AND FIND JOY IN THE PRESENT MOMENT IS...

I WILL TAKE CARE OF MY PHYSICAL AND MENTAL HEALTH BY...

GRATITUDE WITH MY PEEPS

My Peeps

Think about the people in your life and how they make your days a little brighter, maybe even a lot brighter!

This could include friends, family members, neighbors, mentors, coaches, and, since this is your journal, you may even want to include historical figures and modern-day influencers who make you feel all, "YASSS, LET'S GO!"

Peeps Who...

MAKE ME LAUGH

CHEER ME ON

STRETCH MY THINKING

LOVE ME UNCONDITIONALLY

EMBODY GRATEFULNESS

CELEBRATE MY WINS

BRING ME HAPPINESS

GIVE ME COURAGE

I CAN BE SILLY WITH

Top-Drawer Quality Time

As you're enjoying the activities in this section, ponder your peeps and think about how you could use these practices to get to know them better or reconnect with them.

Use the space below to brainstorm ideas for quality one-on-one time with folks you appreciate from your inner circle. Maybe it's a yummy meal, a stroll in a park, or sippin' lattes at a coffee shop. Whatever you decide, the important thing is to be present and give them your total attention.

PRo TIP: This is also a great time to put your devices away. Just sayin'!

VIP's Name	My Idea for QT
☐ CHLOE	TREAT HER TO SOME FRO-YO
☐ _____	_____
☐ _____	_____
☐ _____	_____
☐ _____	_____
☐ _____	_____
☐ _____	_____
☐ _____	_____
☐ _____	_____
☐ _____	_____
☐ _____	_____

" You have been my friend. That in
itself is a tremendous thing. "

E.B. WHITE,

CHARLOTTE TO WILBUR IN *CHARLOTTE'S WEB*

Who Likes Games?

Me! And this is one of my faves for having a good time and upping the closeness with friends and family. It's based on the first set of psychologist Dr. Arthur Aron's 36 Questions, and the deets are below.

MATERIALS:

- **SCISSORS:** Cut out the questions slips on the right

- **CONTAINER:** Bowl, jar, or any other container that's easy to reach into

DIRECTIONS:

1. Fold the question slips in half so there's no peeking, place them in the container, and mix them up.

2. Get a group of people together. (Three or more people is ideal.)

3. Explain that each player will take turns picking a slip of paper from the container and reading the question aloud. The player who picked the question gets to choose someone else to answer it.

4. The person who answers the question can then pick the next slip of paper and ask someone else a question.

5. Have fun, and remember that the point of the game is to get closer!

GIVEN THE CHOICE OF ANYONE IN THE WORLD,
WHOM WOULD YOU WANT AS A DINNER GUEST?

WOULD YOU LIKE TO BE FAMOUS? IN WHAT WAY?

BEFORE MAKING A TELEPHONE CALL, DO YOU EVER REHEARSE
WHAT YOU ARE GOING TO SAY? WHY?

WHAT WOULD CONSTITUTE A "PERFECT" DAY FOR YOU?

WHEN DID YOU LAST SING TO YOURSELF? TO SOMEONE ELSE?

IF YOU WERE ABLE TO LIVE TO THE AGE OF NINETY, RETAINING EITHER THE MIND
OR THE BODY OF A THIRTY-YEAR-OLD, WHICH WOULD YOU WANT?

DO YOU HAVE A SECRET HUNCH ABOUT HOW YOU WILL DIE?

NAME THREE THINGS YOU AND SOMEONE IN THE GROUP APPEAR TO HAVE IN COMMON.

FOR WHAT IN YOUR LIFE DO YOU FEEL MOST GRATEFUL?

IF YOU COULD CHANGE ANYTHING ABOUT THE WAY YOU WERE RAISED,
WHAT WOULD IT BE?

TAKE FOUR MINUTES AND TELL YOUR LIFE STORY IN AS MUCH DETAIL AS POSSIBLE.

IF YOU COULD WAKE UP TOMORROW HAVING GAINED ANY ONE
QUALITY OR ABILITY, WHAT WOULD IT BE?

PRO TIP #1: You can find the full list of Dr. Arthur Aron's 36 Questions with a quick web search. (I have them saved on my phone, too!)

PRO TIP #2: This is a great activity for connecting with people, and you might have more in common with these people than you realize.

The Ultimate Thank-Yous

In the book *The Gratitude Project*, Jeremy Adam Smith reveals that "the richest thank-yous will acknowledge intentions (the pancakes you make when you see I'm hungry) and costs (you massage my feet after work, even when you're really tired), and they'll describe the value of the benefits received (you give me hugs when I'm sad so that I'll feel better)."

Let's give it a go.

Think of something nice someone did for you.

_____

_____

What do you think their intention was?

_____

_____

What do you think this cost them?

_____

_____

What value did this bring to your life?

_____

_____

The Best Darn Thank-You Letter Ever Written in the History of the World

Consider using the stationery on the other side of this page to write an epic gratitude letter that highlights the intention, cost, and value of a gift you have received. See previous page for deets.

When you are finished with your masterpiece, you can:

- CUT IT OUT AND SEND IT VIA THE OLD-FASHIONED POSTAL SERVICE
- HAND DELIVER IT (MAYBE EVEN PLACE IT SOMEWHERE THEY WILL FIND IT—A DELIGHTFUL SURPRISE)
- TAKE A PIC AND TEXT/EMAIL IT TO THEM

If you think they would appreciate it, you could even call them up or visit them and read your letter aloud.

Warning: This activity could cause a salty discharge from your eyes and/or your recipient's!

☐ GRATITUDE IN ACTION: Call, text, email, or mail this person to send them your appreciation and check the box when the mission is completed!

_____
DATE

DEAR _____,

Intentional Acts of Kindness

Think about the important peeps in your life, and come up with some brilliant ways to show 'em some love and make 'em feel special.

Let's get creative and have some fun with it.

	VIP's Name	Act of Kindness
☐	PARKER	COOK HIS FAVE YUMMY MEAL
☐		
☐		
☐		
☐		
☐		
☐		
☐		
☐		
☐		
☐		
☐		
☐		
☐		
☐		
☐		
☐		

Notice, Think, Feel, Do

WHAT DO YOU NOTICE IN YOUR LIFE THAT
YOU CAN BE MEGA GRATEFUL FOR?

THINK REAL HARD ABOUT WHY THE UNIVERSE DROPPED
THIS AMAZING PERSON/PLACE/THING IN YOUR LAP.

HOW DO YOU FEEL ABOUT THE BLESSING/GIFT?

WHAT CAN YOU DO TO SHOW SOME APPRECIATION?

What If...

All right, let's play another game. (Also known as Mental Subtraction, this one comes straight from the amazing minds at UC Berkeley's Greater Good Science Center.)

Think of someone super important in your life right now, and write their name below.

_____

Rewind and think about how you two met. Jot down some of the deets:

_____

_____

_____

_____

Now, imagine a world where this person is not in your life. How would your life be different? Would you have missed out on some amazing experiences or opportunities? Maybe you'd be living a completely different life than the one you have now. It's wild to think about, right? Capture it here:

_____

_____

_____

_____

_____

So, what makes this relationship so special? What are the things that give you all the warm and fuzzies?

_____

_____

_____

_____

Can you imagine how you'd feel if these things weren't there anymore?

_____

_____

_____

_____

But let's not dwell on that! Instead, let's focus on the fact that this person is actually a part of your life right now. How lucky are you?! Let's take a moment to appreciate and feel grateful for that. What are you thinking/feeling?

_____

_____

_____

_____

☐ GRATITUDE IN ACTION: Call, text, or email this person to send them your appreciation and check the box when the mission is completed!

> 66 Feeling gratitude and not expressing it is
> like wrapping a present and not giving it. 99
>
> WILLIAM ARTHUR WARD

Gratitude Their Way

There are typically three main ways that we experience and express gratitude:

- CONNECTIONS (QUALITY TIME WITH EACH OTHER)
- WORDS (WRITTEN OR SPOKEN)
- GIFTS (OR DOING KIND THINGS)

You can think of them as different flavors of gratitude, and people tend to have their fave flavor. Some people prefer rocky road, while others prefer butter pecan.

Think about the people in your life, and brainstorm how you can show them gratitude in their favorite flavor.

Those who love connection...

	VIP's Name	Ways I Can Connect
☐	BLAKE	GO TO THE PARK AND PLAY BASKETBALL
☐		
☐		
☐		

Those who love words...

       VIP's Name   Things I Can Say

☐ _____   _____

☐ _____   _____

☐ _____   _____

Those who love gifts...

       VIP's Name   Something I Can Give

☐ _____   _____

☐ _____   _____

☐ _____   _____

Keep in mind: Even a chocoholic could be in the mood for rainbow sherbet, so don't be afraid to mix it up, and when in doubt, it doesn't hurt to ask what your VIP prefers!

" Let us be grateful to the people who make us happy; they are the charming gardeners who make our souls blossom. **"**

MARCEL PROUST

Pick Your Prompt

When you are in the mood to free-write, pick a prompt from below and respond using the blank-ish pages that follow. You could cut the prompt out and glue or tape it on the page, giving yourself as much space as you need/want to respond. If the idea of cutting your journal stresses you out, feel free to rewrite the prompts instead.

A PERSON WHO STRAIGHT-UP MAKES MY LIFE BETTER IS...

ONE THING I SERIOUSLY ADORE ABOUT ONE OF MY FRIENDS IS...

TODAY, I GET TO HANG OUT WITH...

WHEN I'M HAVING A TOTAL DUMPSTER FIRE OF A DAY,
SOMEONE WHO GIVES ME HOPE IS...

SOMEONE DID SOMETHING SMALL, BUT IT TOTALLY MADE ME JOYFUL WHEN...

I CAN'T WAIT TO GIVE A BIG OL' THANK-YOU TO...

SOMEONE WHO WOULD BE STOKED TO GET A HANDWRITTEN NOTE
OR LETTER FROM ME IS... I'D TELL THEM...

TODAY, I'M GONNA SHOW MY PEEPS SOME LOVE AND GRATITUDE.
WHEN THEY LEAST EXPECT IT, I'M GONNA...

SOMEONE WHO'S LIKE A HUMAN JETPACK PROPELLING ME TO SOAR
TO NEW HEIGHTS OF GREATNESS IS...

SOMEONE WHO IS IN DIRE NEED OF MY UNDIVIDED ATTENTION TODAY IS...

I'M FEELING SUPER GRATEFUL FOR ALL THE LOVE AND SUPPORT FROM...

A TIME THAT SOMEONE'S KINDNESS MADE ME FEEL LIKE A TOTAL VIP WAS...

PRO TIP: You can pick a new prompt each time, return to your fave(s), or both.

Reflections

Think about your last week or month.

How's it been going?

A HIGHLIGHT WAS...

A CHALLENGE WAS...

MY MOOD WAS BEST WHEN
I WAS AROUND...

SOMETHING THAT I'VE
RECENTLY LEARNED ABOUT MY
RELATIONSHIP(S) IS...

Intentions

Think about your next week or month.

What will you make happen in your relationships?

SOMETHING THAT I'VE BEEN PUTTING OFF THAT I CAN DO TODAY TO IMPROVE A RELATIONSHIP IS...

I WILL FOCUS ON CONNECTING WITH A FRIEND OR LOVED ONE BY...

ONE WAY I WILL APPRECIATE CONNECTIONS, WORDS, AND GIFTS WITH OTHERS IN THE PRESENT MOMENT IS...

I WILL TAKE CARE OF SOMEONE I CARE ABOUT BY...

GRATITUDE WITH THE WORLD

WHAT DO YOU NOTICE IN YOUR LIFE THAT
YOU CAN BE MEGA GRATEFUL FOR?

THINK REAL HARD ABOUT WHY THE UNIVERSE DROPPED
THIS AMAZING PERSON/PLACE/THING IN YOUR LAP.

HOW DO YOU FEEL ABOUT THE BLESSING/GIFT?

WHAT CAN YOU DO TO SHOW SOME APPRECIATION?

The "Spreading Good Vibes" Checklist

Let's do something lovely for others on purpose!

Here's a fun and easy-peasy checklist of nice things you can do to spread some love and kindness around.

- [ ] HOLD THE DOOR OPEN FOR SOMEONE LIKE A CHAMP.
- [ ] TELL A STRANGER THAT THEIR HAIR IS ON POINT OR THEIR SMILE IS MAKIN' YOUR DAY.
- [ ] SURPRISE THE PERSON IN LINE BEHIND YOU BY BUYING THEM A TASTY TREAT OR A HOT BREW.
- [ ] FLEX YOUR MUSCLES AND HELP CARRY SOMEONE'S HEAVY BAGS.
- [ ] BE A STELLAR LISTENER AND LEND AN EAR TO SOMEONE WHO NEEDS TO CHAT OR VENT.
- [ ] SEND A CARE PACKAGE TO MEMBERS OF THE MILITARY SERVING OVERSEAS.
- [ ] SHOWER EVERYONE YOU MEET WITH GENUINE COMPLIMENTS ALL DAY LONG.
- [ ] LACE UP THOSE SNEAKERS AND JOIN A CHARITY RUN TO FEEL GOOD AND DO GOOD.
- [ ] ROLL UP YOUR SLEEVES AND VOLUNTEER AT A SOUP KITCHEN.
- [ ] DECLUTTER YOUR BOOKSHELF AND DONATE SOME BOOKS TO YOUR LOCAL LIBRARY TO SPREAD THE JOY OF READING.
- [ ] SHOW SOME LOVE TO THE UNSUNG HEROES IN YOUR COMMUNITY BY WRITING A SWEET THANK-YOU NOTE TO YOUR MAIL CARRIER, FIREFIGHTERS, LIBRARIANS, AND NEIGHBORS.
- [ ] BE A BOSS AND HELP CLEAN UP YOUR NEIGHBORHOOD BY PICKING UP LITTER AND LEAVING IT BETTER THAN YOU FOUND IT.

☐ LEARN ABOUT LOCAL AND GLOBAL ISSUES TO SEE HOW YOU CAN HELP MAKE THINGS BETTER.

☐ BE A SHOPPING CART SUPERHERO AND RETURN THOSE BUGGIES TO THEIR DESIGNATED AREAS TO MAKE LIFE EASIER FOR OTHERS.

Even small acts of kindness can have a big impact on someone's day, so have a blast making the world a better place, one intentional good deed at a time!

"No one has ever become poor by giving."

ANNE FRANK

> **"** Every act of love is a work of
> peace no matter how small. **"**
>
> SAINT MOTHER TERESA

A Little Goes a Long Way

Cut out these cute little thank-you notes and carry them with you. When you catch someone else spreading good vibes, pass them a note!

Here are some other people to consider giving a note to:

- THE TRAFFIC ANGEL WHO STOPS TO LET SOMEONE CROSS THE STREET SAFELY

- THE BARISTA WHO'S A DAILY DOSE OF SUNSHINE

- THE PATIENT PERSON WHO LETS OTHERS GO AHEAD IN LINE AT THE STORE

- THE COMPLIMENTS COMMANDER WHO BOOSTED SOMEONE'S MOOD WITH GENUINE WORDS

- THE PERSON WALKING BY WHO OFFERS TO TAKE A PHOTO FOR SOMEONE WHO'S STRUGGLING TO TAKE A SELFIE

- THE KIND SOUL WHO SMILES AND SAYS "HELLO" TO SOMEONE THEY PASS BY ON THE STREET

"Do your little bit of good where you are; it's those little bits of good put together that overwhelm the world."

DESMOND TUTU

The Reviews Are In

The next time you go to the grocery store and see those stocked shelves, think of how many people it took to make that possible:

- FARMERS
- FACTORY WORKERS
- TRUCK DRIVERS
- GROCERY STORE WORKERS (TO NAME A FEW!)

Thanks to these hardworking people, we have access to healthy food.

And even though we don't always know everyone involved, there are some real MVPs we get to connect with.

Let's learn their names, show some gratitude, and give them some love by leaving a thoughtful review online. They deserve it!

Who's "they"? Think about all the services that you use in your life and all the opportunities to publicly show gratitude for those people:

- HEALTH-CARE WORKERS
- SALESPEOPLE
- FOOD SERVERS
- HAIRDRESSERS
- HOUSE CLEANERS
- FOOD-DELIVERY DRIVERS
- MECHANICS
- AND MANY MORE!

You could make someone's day and also feel great about yourself for putting a little positivity out into the world. Maybe something like this:

I recently had the most _____
(ADJECTIVE)

service at _____
(COMPANY/RESTAURANT/STORE NAME)

The staff was incredibly _____.
(ADJECTIVE)

They went above and beyond to make my experience _____.
(ADJECTIVE)

I was particularly impressed by _____
(SPECIFIC DETAIL OR EMPLOYEE THAT STOOD OUT)

Overall, I had a _____ time
(ADJECTIVE)

and would highly recommend _____
(COMPANY/RESTAURANT/STORE NAME)

to anyone looking for _____ _____.
(ADJECTIVE)   (PRODUCT OR SERVICE)

☐ GRATITUDE IN ACTION: Post an online review!

" Alone we can do so little.
Together we can do so much.**"**

HELEN KELLER

Pick Your Prompt

When you are in the mood to free-write, pick a prompt from below and respond using the blank-ish pages that follow. You could cut the prompt out and glue or tape it on the page, giving yourself as much space as you need/want to respond. If the idea of cutting your journal stresses you out, feel free to rewrite the prompts instead.

ONE THING THAT REALLY GETS ME OUT OF BED IN THE MORNING IS...

AT ITS PEAK AWESOMENESS, THE WORLD WOULD...

TO SPREAD LOVE AND HAPPINESS, I...

ONE WAY I CAN USE MY AWESOME, UNIQUE TALENTS TO MAKE THE WORLD A BETTER PLACE IS...

ONE TINY THING I CAN DO TODAY TO MAKE THE WORLD AT LEAST A SMIDGE BETTER IS...

I WAS BLESSED BY SOMEONE'S GENEROSITY WHEN...

A TIME WHEN I'VE DONE SOMETHING SUPER NICE FOR SOMEONE AND FELT LIKE A SUPERHERO AFTERWARD WAS...

I CAN STEP UP MY GAME WHEN IT COMES TO TAKING CARE OF THE PEEPS AND THINGS I HOLD DEAR BY...

I CAN LEVEL UP MY GENEROSITY GAME AND SHARE THE WEALTH BY...

IF I HAD TWENTY-FOUR HOURS LEFT TO LIVE, I WOULD MAKE IT THE MOST EPIC DAY EVER BY...

I SPREAD SOME KINDNESS TODAY WHEN I...

PRO TIP: You can pick a new prompt each time, return to your fave(s), or both.

Reflections

Think about your last week or month.
How's it been going?

A HIGHLIGHT WAS...

A CHALLENGE WAS...

AN ACT OF KINDNESS (BIG
OR SMALL) THAT I WITNESSED
OR PERFORMED WAS...

SOMETHING THAT I'VE
RECENTLY LEARNED ABOUT
DOING GOOD DEEDS IS...

Intentions

Think about your next week or month.

What will you make happen in your community?

SOMETHING THAT I'VE BEEN
PUTTING OFF THAT I
CAN DO TODAY...

I WILL FOCUS ON CONNECTING
WITH MY COMMUNITY BY...

ONE WAY I WILL APPRECIATE MY
COMMUNITY AND FIND JOY IN
THE PRESENT MOMENT IS...

I WILL DO SOMETHING GOOD
FOR MY COMMUNITY...

Vision Board:
Living in Gratitude

· ·

· ·

For all I know, you've arrived at this page before you've actually done
anything in your journal. That's bold! No matter where you are in your
journal journey, you are doing it. Good for you!

I invite you to use this space to gather images, quotes, aha moments, and anything else that speaks to your ultimate vision for living gratefully.

Now take your vision and turn it into actions! You got this!

" Gratitude makes sense of our past, brings peace for today, and creates a vision for tomorrow. **"**

MELODY BEATTIE

ABOUT LAINIE ROWELL

Lainie Rowell is a bestselling author, award-winning educator, and TEDx speaker. She is dedicated to human flourishing, focusing on community building, social emotional learning, and honoring what makes each of us unique and dynamic. She earned her degree in psychology and went on to earn postgraduate degrees in education. As an international speaker and a consultant, Lainie's client list ranges from Fortune 100 companies like Apple and Google to school districts and independent schools.

For more: **LainieRowell.com**

ABOUT ALLYSON LIU

Allyson Liu is a creative talent who discovered her passion for design early on. She has extensive experience in industries such as publishing and advertising. She also founded How Inviting, a line of custom stationery, which gained national attention when it was featured on NBC's *Today Show*. Now, Allyson helps clients achieve their marketing goals through her company Allyson Liu, Marketing + Creative, where she brings a unique and inspired approach to branding.

For more: **AllysonLiu.com**

Made in United States
Troutdale, OR
11/15/2024

24875215R00090